THIS COPY OF

THE Wobbly Jelly JOKE BOOK

BELONGS TO

sarah Barnes

Also in Sparrow by Jim Eldridge
The Funniest Joke Book

The Wobbly Jelly JOKE BOOK

Compiled by
Jim Eldridge
illustrated by
Colin West

SPARROW
BOOKS

A Sparrow Book
Published by Arrow Books Limited
17–21 Conway Street, London W1P 6JD

An imprint of the Hutchinson Publishing Group

London Melbourne Sydney Auckland
Johannesburg and agencies throughout the world

First published 1984

Text © Jim Eldridge 1984
Illustrations © Colin West 1984

Set in Linoterm Baskerville by
JH Graphics Ltd, Reading

Made and printed in Great Britain
by the Anchor Press Ltd
Tiptree, Essex

ISBN 0 09 938160 5

Introduction

With special thanks for all their help to the children and staffs of Warden Hill Junior, Farley Hill Junior, and Lady Zia Wernher Schools, Luton; to the staff at Dunstable Library; to 'Uncle Badger' of the Dunstable Gazette/Luton News; and to The Book Castle, Dunstable, without whose help and contributions this book would never have happened.

Jim Eldridge

What car is like a sausage?
An old banger.

What's bright yellow and dangerous?
Shark-infested custard.

There was a man who had a blancmange in one ear and a jelly in the other. He was a trifle deaf.

Why is a banana skin like a pullover?
Because it's easy to slip on.

What did the grape say when the elephant trod on it?
It just gave out a little wine.

Why do bakers work so hard?
Because they knead the dough.

What stays hot even in the fridge?
Mustard.

MAN: I want six slices of bacon, and make them lean.
BUTCHER: *Certainly, sir. Which way?*

What flies and wobbles?
A jellycopter.

What does a vegetarian cannibal eat?
Swedes.

What's white and fluffy and swings from cake-shop to cake-shop?
A meringue-utang.

Why are cooks cruel?
Because they beat eggs, whip cream, and batter fish.

Knock knock.
– *Who's there?*
Irish stew.
– *Irish stew who?*
Irish stew in the name of the Law.

9

Two ears of corn were running up a hill. What were they when they got to the top?
Puffed wheat.

What did the chocolate say to the lollipop?
'Hi-yah, sucker!'

How do you work out the colour of plums?
Use a green gauge.

TEACHER: What minerals are found in Cornwall?
BOY: *Coca Cola and Orangeade.*

Why did the egg go into the jungle?
Because it was an eggsplorer.

If an egg came floating down the Mississippi
River, where would it have come from?
From a chicken.

How can you improve the taste of salt?
Sprinkle it lightly over chips.

Why do people never starve in the desert?
Because of the sand-which-is there.

How do monkeys know the date?
They eat it.

If you get a referee in boxing, a referee in rugby,
and a referee in football, what do you get in
bowls?
Soup.

How do you stop a fish from smelling?
Cut its nose off.

Definition of baked beans on toast: skinheads on
a raft.

Why did the jelly wobble?
Because it saw the milk shake.

Why is bread like champagne?
It's good for toasting.

How can you tell that a wedding cake is sad?
Because of its tiers.

When is spaghetti a disappointment?
When it's mockoroni.

What's green and hairy and goes up and down?
A gooseberry in a lift.

What sort of meat do karate experts prefer?
Chops.

What sort of fish do cobblers prefer?
Sole.

What is brown, sticky and shocking?
Electric treacle.

What has knobs on and wobbles?
Jellyvision.

What's purple and round and floats up in the sky?
The planet of the grapes.

When is soup musical?
When it's piping hot.

Why did the elephant sit on the tomato?
It wanted to play squash.

What type of cake do children dislike?
A cake of soap.

TEACHER: There was the Ice Age, then the Stone Age. What came next?
GIRL: *The saus-age.*

What's the best day for cooking eggs and bacon?
Fryday.

A woman woke her husband up and said, 'There's a burglar in the kitchen eating the cake I made this afternoon. Ring 999!' 'Who shall I ask for?' said her husband, 'police or ambulance?'

What do you call a carrot who insults a farmer?
A fresh vegetable.

What's red and juicy and goes putt-putt-putt?
An outboard tomato.

How do you start a pudding race?
Sago!

Which side of an apple is the left side?
The side that hasn't been eaten.

What do ghosts eat for supper?
Ghoulash.

— Eat up your spinach. It'll put colour in your cheeks.
— *Who wants green cheeks?*

FIRST WOMAN: *I baked a sponge cake today, but it was a failure.*
SECOND WOMAN: Why was that?
FIRST WOMAN: *The chemist sold me the wrong sponges.*

My Dad is such a bad cook he even burns salad.

Mum, there's a black cat in the kitchen.
– That's all right, black cats are lucky.
Not this one, he's just eaten Dad's dinner.

What is the difference between a young lady and a fresh loaf?
One is a well-bred maid and the other is well-made bread.

What is the fastest vegetable?
A runner bean.

Why does the apple tree cry?
Because people always pick on it.

Knock knock.
– Who's there?
Exam.
– Exam who?
Eggs, ham and cheese.

What do policemen like in their sandwiches?
Truncheon meat.

Knock knock.
— Who's there?
Four eggs.
— Four eggs who?
For eggsample.

Did you hear about the two prunes who were arrested for being stewed?
They were remanded in custardy.

Who was round and purple and ruled Russia?
Peter the Grape.

What's green, covered in custard, and miserable?
Apple grumble.

What is round, red and cheeky?
Tomato sauce.

What do witches have for breakfast?
Snap cackle and pop.

The sausage is a cunning bird
With feathers long and wavy;
It swims about the frying pan
And makes its nest in gravy.

Why did the farmer go over his potatoes with a
heavy roller?
Because he wanted mashed potatoes.

What's purple and hums?
An electric prune.

What do you get if you cross a cow with a duck?
Cream quackers.

How can you tell when an elephant's been in the
fridge?
By the footprints in the butter.

Knock knock.
– Who's there?
Banana.
– Banana who?
Knock knock.
– Who's there?
Banana.
– Banana who?
Knock knock.
– Who's there?
Banana
– Banana who?
Knock knock.
– Who's there?
Orange.
– Orange who?
Orange you glad I didn't say banana!

What do you call a Welsh apple?
Taffy apple.

What's short and green and goes camping?
A boy sprout.

What's chocolate outside, peanut inside, and
sings hymns?
A Sunday School Treet.

What vegetables do plumers fix?
Leeks.

What would happen if pigs could fly?
The price of bacon would go up.

How do you start a jelly race?
Get set.

How do you spell hungry horse in four letters?
MTGG.

Knock knock.
– Who's there?
Egbert.
– Egbert who?
Egg but no bacon.

It's fun to watch people eating jumping-bean pie;
They aim at their mouth but it lands in their eye.

What is green and bounces?
A spring onion.

Knock knock.
– Who's there?
Lettuce.
– Lettuce who?
Lettuce in and you'll find out.

Why did the girl keep a loaf of bread in her comic?
She liked crumby jokes.

What sugar sings?
I-sing sugar.

What can a whole orange do but half an orange can't?
Look round.

What cheese is made backwards?
Edam.

If cheese comes after dinner, what comes after cheese?
Mice.

Why did the boy take the sugar and milk to the cinema?
Because they were showing a cereal.

What's the difference between an elephant and a biscuit?
You can't dip an elephant in your tea.

What stands on one leg and has its heart on its head?
A cabbage.

There were two eggs in a saucepan. One egg said, 'Whoo, it's hot in here.' The other one said, 'Wait till you get out, you'll get your head bashed in.'

Shall I tell you the joke about the butter?
I'd better not, you might spread it.

Two biscuits were walking down the road. One got run over. What did the other say?
'Crumbs!'

Why can't you put an elephant in a sandwich?
Because it'd be too heavy to lift.

What flies around the kitchen at 600kph and glows yellow?
An unidentified flying omelette.

Why did the banana split?
Because it saw the apple turnover.

What fills a field with music?
Popcorn.

What happened when there was a fight in the fish shop?
Two fish got battered.

What's the best butter in the world?
A goat.

What's yellow and dangerous?
A banana with a machine gun.

Why did the tomato blush?
Because it saw the salad dressing.

What animals in Noah's Ark didn't come in pairs?
Worms, they came in apples.

What do you get when you cross an orange and a squash court?
Orange squash.

What is the best thing to put into a cake?
Your teeth.

What's the favourite meal of nuclear scientists?
Fission chips.

What pear can't you eat?
A pair of shoes.

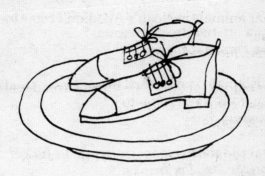

What's worse than finding a maggot in your apple?
Finding half a maggot

How do you remove a peanut from your ear?
Pour chocolate in it; it will come out a Treet.

What did the orange say to the other orange on
the phone?
Nothing, the pips went.

When are the streets greasiest?
When the rain is dripping.

Which plant can be used in sandwiches and is
dangerous if you run into it?
A hambush.

What did the mayonnaise say to the fridge?
'Close the door, I'm dressing.'

How do you make a sausage roll?
Push it.

How do you know a sausage doesn't like being fried?
Because it spits.

What room has no floor or ceiling, windows or doors?
A mushroom.

A man was at a party talking to a woman and eating salad. The man's son came up and said 'Dad, dad!' but his father said 'Don't interrupt me when I'm talking' and carried on. When the man had finished he said to his son 'Now, what was it you were going to say?' and the boy said 'I was trying to tell you there was a slug on your lettuce, but it doesn't matter now, you've eaten it.'

Why has that pig got a wooden leg?
— *That pig saved my life once.*
What did it do?
— *When the house caught fire, it rang the fire brigade.*
But that doesn't answer why it's got a wooden leg.
— *When you've got a pig as good as that you don't eat it all at once.*

GRANNY: If you don't eat your porridge you won't grow up to be a beautiful lady.

GIRL: *Didn't you eat your porridge, Granny?*

Why don't elephants like penguins?
Because they can't get the silver paper off.

What did they call the two monks who worked in the monastery kitchen?
The Fish Friar and the Chip Monk.

Which fish sleeps a lot?
A kipper.

What do bees do with honey?
They cell it.

What do you call two rows of cabbages?
A dual cabbageway.

Why couldn't the orange get up the hill?
Because it had run out of juice.

What is the main ingredient of dog biscuits?
Collie-flour.

What sort of food do fighter pilots prefer?
Scrambled eggs.

What sort of breakfast do comedians prefer?
Cornflakes.

Which fish is very musical?
A piano tuna.

What sort of breakfast do birds prefer?
Shredded tweet

What sort of vegetables do athletes prefer?
Runner beans.

What sort of vegetables do watchmakers prefer?
Spring greens.

Who owns all the milk in Saudi Arabia?
A milk sheik.

What is bald and wobbles?
Jelly Savalas.

Definition of a sandwich-man: Snack for a cannibal.

What does a vegetarian vampire eat?
Blood oranges.

Who swings through the vines?
Tarzan of the grapes.

How can you help a deaf fisherman?
Give him a herring aid.

What is brown, hairy and bashful?
A coconut shy.

Why do elephants paint their feet yellow?
So they can hide upside down in custard.

When do elephants paint their toe-nails red?
When they want to hide in strawberry jam.

What's the difference between a mouldy lettuce and a dismal song?
One's a bad salad and the other's a sad ballad.

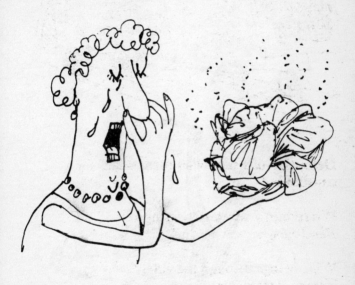

What do you do if you find a blue banana?
Cheer it up.

What's green on the outside and yellow on the inside?
A banana disguised as a cucumber.

What did the cannibal have for lunch?
Baked beings on toast.

What would you call a train loaded with sweets?
A chew-chew train.

What fruit do you find on coins?
Dates.

If a crocodile makes shoes, what does a banana make?
Slippers.

What is yellow, soft and goes round and round?
A long-playing omelette.

A cannibal came home to find his wife cutting up a small native and a boa constrictor. 'Oh no,' he said, 'not snake and pygmy pie again!'

What did the hamburger say to the tomato?
'That's enough of your sauce.'

What do scientists eat?
Microchips.

BOY: *Mum, can I have twenty pence for an old man crying outside in the street?*
MUM: Of course. What's he crying about?
BOY: *Toffee apples – twenty pence each.*

Why didn't the banana snore?
Because it was afraid to wake up the rest of the bunch.

What is 300 feet high and wobbles?
The trifle tower.

What are hot, greasy and romantic?
Chips that pass in the night.

FIRST CAT: How did you get on in the milk-drinking contest?
SECOND CAT: *I won by six laps.*

What do ghosts have for breakfast?
Dreaded wheat.

What goes ABCDEFGHIJKLMNOPQRSTU-VWXYZ slurp?
A man eating alphabet soup.

Why did the orange go to the doctor?
Because it wasn't peeling very well.

What vegetable plays snooker?
A cue-cumber.

MUM: **Don't you know you're not supposed to eat with your knife?**
CHILD: *Yes, but my fork leaks.*

What is yellow and flickers?
A lemon with a loose connection.

How do you make golden vegetable soup?
Use fourteen carats.

Knock knock.
– Who's there?
Whale meat.
– Whale meat who?
Whale meat again.

'Who's been eating my porridge?' said Baby
Bear.
'Who's been eating my porridge?' said Mummy
Bear.
'Burp!' said Daddy Bear.

Who makes spells in a cafe?
A sandwitch.

What do French people eat for breakfast?
Huit heures bix.

PATIENT: Doctor, I feel like an ice-cream.
DOCTOR: *So do I. Get me one too.*

My Dad's cooking is so bad you can't even get your fork into the gravy.

What does a traffic warden have in his sandwiches?
Traffic jam.

What is yellow and white and travels at 90mph?
A train driver's egg sandwich.

What runs round Paris at noon wrapped in
cellophane?
The lunchpack of Notre Dame.

If there are two tomatoes on horseback, which
one is the cowboy?
Neither, they're both redskins.

What is yellow and points north?
A magnetic banana.

Who plays the bagpipes while cooking chips?
The Frying Scotsman.

What is yellow and has twenty-two legs?
Banana United.

Why do idiots eat biscuits?
Because they're crackers.

'We had my Granny for Christmas dinner last year.'
'Oh? We had turkey.'

Why don't they grow bananas any longer?
Because they're long enough already.

What do cannibal children like playing best?
Swallow my leader.

'Doctor, can you give me something for my liver?'?
'How about a pound of onions.'

What letter is a vegetable?
P.

How can you tell when there's an elephant in your custard?
When it's especially lumpy.

Why wouldn't the man eat apples?
Because his Granny had died of apple-plexy.

Why do Eskimos eat candles?
Because they prefer light meals.

When does an astronaut have his midday meal?
At launch time.

What is a vampire's favourite soup?
Scream of tomato.

What is purple and 4000 miles long?
The Grape Wall of China.

How do you know when you're eating rabbit stew?
When it's got hares in it.

'*That new restaurant for idiots has got an interesting item on its menu.*'
'*What's that?*'
'*Soup in a basket.*'

Knock knock.
– Who's there?
Soup.
– Soup who?
Souperman.

What do frogs drink?
Croaka Cola.

Why shouldn't you tell secrets in a vegetable garden?
Because the corn has ears and beans talk.

TEACHER: Name ten things with milk in them.
CHILD: *Milk-shake, tea, coffee and seven cows.*

What is a meatball?
A dance in a butcher's shop.

What's yellow and stupid?
Thick custard.

Fred was having tea with his Granny. 'Would you like some bread and butter, Fred?' she asked. 'Yes thank you, Gran,' said Fred. 'That's a good boy. I like to hear you say "thank you".' 'If you want to hear me say it again you might put some jam on it,' said Fred.

What do cannibal guests eat for lunch?
Buttered host.

Why is history the sweetest lesson?
Because it's full of dates.

MUM: There were two chocolate cakes in the
larder yesterday, and now there's only one.
Why?
CHILD: *It must have been so dark I didn't see the other
one.*

Which rich Arab invented flavoured crips?
Sultan Vinegar.

50

What did the lion say when it saw two hunters in a jeep?
'Hooray it's Meals on Wheels!'

A man was standing eating fish and chips. Next to him was a lady with a little dog, which became excited at the smell of the man's food and began whining and jumping up at him. 'Do you mind if I throw him a bit?' asked the man. 'Not at all,' said the lady, pleased. So the man picked the dog up and threw it over a wall.

How do you stop meatballs from drowning?
Put them in gravy boats.

A tramp knocked at a door and asked for food. 'Didn't I give you some of my home-made pie a week ago?' said the woman who answered the door. 'Yes,' said the tramp, 'but I'm a lot better now.'

What did the donkey say when it only had thistles to eat?
'Thistle have to do.'

What's yellow and goes round and round and round?
A banana in a washing machine.

Did you hear about the missionary who went to Africa, and gave the cannibals their first taste of Christianity?

A very mean man took his family into a restaurant for sausages and chips. After the meal there were two sausages left over and the man told the waiter: 'I'll take them home for the dog.' Immediately one of his children shouted, 'Hooray, we're going to get a dog!'

What's yellow and goes click-click?
A ball-point banana.

Where were chips first fried?
In Greece.

What do jelly-babies wear on their feet?
Gum boots.

When is a red-headed idiot like a biscuit?
When he's a ginger-nut.

'What happened to all those cakes? I told you
you couldn't have one, and now there's only one
left.'
'That's the one I haven't had.'

There was a man who was put on a diet of
bananas and coconut milk for three months. He
didn't lose any weight, but by the end of it he
couldn't half climb trees!

What do you get if you cross a citrus fruit with a
bell?
An orange that can peal itself.

Did you hear about the man at the supermarket who was leaning over the frozen food counter when five fish fingers reached up and strangled him?

Where would you find exploding spaghetti?
At the Minestrone of Defence.

'Why do you keep doing the back-stroke?'
'I've just had dinner and I don't want to swim on a full stomach.'

Why did the cat eat the cheese?
So it could blow down the mouse hole with baited breath.

What dog has no tail?
A hotdog.

What cake is dangerous?
Attila the Bun.

What did the cheese biscuits say to the almonds?
You're nuts and we're crackers.

What tree has the best food?
A pantry.

GRANNY: What would you like?
CHILD: *Cake.*
GRAN: Cake what?
CHILD: *Cake first.*

What nut has no shell?
A doughnut.

What did the astronaut see in his frying pan?
An unidentified frying object.

'John, have you finished your alphabet soup?'
Not yet, I'm only up to the Ms.

How do you know that coconut juice is nutty?
Because it lives in a padded cell.

GIRL: Boo-hoo, I made a lovely meat pie and the cat's eaten it.
BROTHER: *Never mind, Mum'll buy us another cat.*

'Eat your dinner.'
'I'm waiting for the mustard to cool.'

What do pixies have for tea?
Fairy cakes.

What's the fastest thing in the world?
Milk — it's pasteurised before you see it.

What happened to the man who dreamed he was eating a giant marshmallow?
When he woke up his pillow had disappeared.

What is a ghost's favourite dessert?
Ice-scream.

What turns without moving?
Milk — when it turns sour.

What do you get if you cross a cow with a camel?
Lumpy milk shakes.

Where do baby apes sleep?
In apricots.

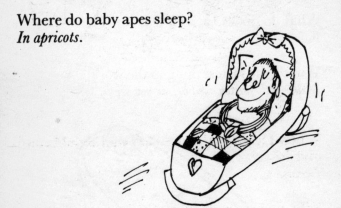

Why did the lazy man get a job in a bakery?
Because he wanted a good loaf.

What's Chinese and deadly?
Chop sueycide.

Why are bakers good people?
Because they earn an honest crust.

What do Italian ghosts have for lunch?
Spooketti.

When a lemon calls for help, what should you give it?
Lemonade.

Why do bees have sticky hair?
Because they have honey combs.

Why did the man cross a chicken with an octopus?
So all his family could have a leg each.

There was a man who was so mean he kept a fork in the sugar bowl.

Did you hear about the red sauce chasing the
brown sauce?
It couldn't ketchup.'

What did the flour say when it fell over?
Don't pick me up, I'm self-raising.

What nut sounds like a sneeze?
Cashoo.

What is a frog's favourite sweet?
A lollihop.

TEACHER: What is the climate like in New
   Zealand?
CHILD: *Very very cold.*
TEACHER: What makes you say that?
CHILD: *Well, when they send us meat it always arrives
   frozen.*

What do you get if you cross a pig with a zebra?
Striped sausages.

What did one strawberry say to the other strawberry?
Between you and me, we shouldn't have got into this jam.

Knock knock.
– Who's there?
Arthur.
– Arthur who?
Arthur any biscuits left?

Why did the apple turnover?
Because it saw the swiss roll.

What do mermaids eat for breakfast?
Marmalade on toast.

TEACHER: I'm afraid your son has swallowed 50p
TEACHER: *That's all right, it was his dinner money.*

What do you call a man who steals cattle?
A beefburglar.

'This morning my Mum gave me soap-flakes instead of cornflakes.'
'I bet you were mad.'
'Mad? I was foaming at the mouth.'

Knock knock.
– Who's there?
Marmite.
– Marmite who?
Marmite but Pa might not.

CHILD: I don't like cheese with holes in it.
MUM: *Just eat the cheese and leave the holes on the side of your plate.*

What do you get if you cross a football team with an ice-cream?
Aston Vanilla.

What kind of person is fed up with people?
A cannibal.

A man saw a gardener pushing a wheelbarrow filled with manure. 'Where are you going with that?' he asked. 'I'm going to put it on my rhubarb,' said the gardener. 'Suit yourself,' the man replied, 'I put custard on mine.'

What cereal does an Eskimo have for breakfast?
Snowflakes.

What is woolly, covered in chocolate and goes round the sun?
A Mars Baaaaa.

What do you get if you run over a canary with a lawn-mower?
Shredded tweet.

What go squeak-squeak when you pour milk over them?
Mice crispies.

What is coq au vin?
A chicken on a lorry.

What's green and runs up the wall?
A runner bean.

What did the chef do when a customer fainted?
Gave her the quiche of life.

What did the dentist say when his wife baked a cake?
'Can I do the filling?'

What should you do for a starving cannibal?
Give him a hand.

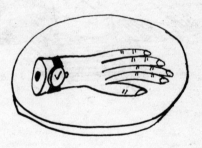

What do vampires put on their roast beef?
Grave-y.

What did one chick say to the other chick when it found an orange in their nest?
Look at the orange Mama laid.

What is most like half an orange?
The other half.

How do you stop a cock from crowing on
Sunday?
Eat it on Saturday.

What is green and holds up stage-coaches?
Dick Gherkin.

VEGETARIAN: I've lived on nothing but
vegetables for years.
LISTENER: *So what, I've lived on Earth all my life.*

What's yellow and goes slam-slam-slam-slam?
A four-door banana.

MAN: *I don't like this pie.*
LANDLADY: Oh don't you. I'll have you know I
was making pies before you were born.
MAN: *Perhaps this is one of them.*

What do you get if you pour boiling water down
a rabbit hole?
Hot cross bunnies.

Why are bananas never lonely?
Because they hang around in bunches.

'This loaf is nice and warm.'
'It should be – the cat's been sitting on it.'

*'Have you heard the story about the cornflake and the
shredded wheat?'*
'No.'
'I'll tell you on Sunday, it's a wheat-ly cereal.'

Why did the woman get a shock when she picked up a bun?
The currant ran up her arm.

What is yellow and goes up and down?
A lemon in a lift.

'Two pounds of cats' meat, please.'
'Certainly sir. Shall I wrap it or will you eat it here?'

What do ghosts drink?
Demonade.

What does a vegetarian earn?
A celery.

What do you get if you put springs on a cow?
Milk shakes.

What kind of meringues show their disapproval?
Boo-meringues.

Why is a pork-pie hat uncomfortable to wear?
Because the gravy runs down your neck.

WOMAN: Have you got a sheep's head?
BUTCHER: *No, madam, it's the way I part my hair.*

What's brown, hairy and wears sunglasses?
A coconut on holiday.

Why did the peanut complain to the police?
Because he'd been assaulted.

GRANNY: You've left all your crusts, Joan. When
I was your age I ate every one.
JOAN: *Do you still like crusts, Grandma?*
GRANNY: Yes I do.
JOAN: *Well, you can have mine.*

What lies in a pram and wobbles?
A jelly baby.

Why did the biscuit cry?
Because its Mum had been a wafer so long.

What sits in a fruit bowl and shouts for help?
A damson in distress.

'Gran's cooking Sunday lunch for us.'
'Yuk! I suppose that means Enthusiasm Soup again.'
'What's Enthusiasm Soup?'
'She puts everything she's got into it.'

The waitress brought Mr Jones his soup, and
then stood looking out of the window.
'It looks like rain,' she said.
'Yes,' replied Mr Jones having started his soup, 'it tastes
like rain as well.'

What's sweet, white and fluffy, has whiskers,
and floats?
A catameringue.

What do sea monsters eat?
Fish and ships.

What do you get if you cross a potato with an onion?
A spud with watery eyes.

How do you cook toast in the jungle?
Under a gorilla.

'Have you heard the joke about the eggs?'
'No.'
'Two bad.'

What do you get if you cross a hyena with an Oxo cube?
An animal that makes a laughing stock of itself.

TEACHER (on school dinner duty): Any complaints?

CHILD: *Yes sir, these peas are too hard.*

TEACHER (dipping a spoon into the peas, and tasting them): They seem soft enough to me.

CHILD: *They are now. I've been chewing them for the last half hour.*

VICAR: Do you say your prayers before dinner, John?

JOHN: *No sir, my Mum's a good cook.*

What's the difference between a piano and a fish?
You can't tuna fish.

What do porcupines have for dinner?
Prickled onions.

What is the French word for dentures?
Aperitif.

MUM: Don't you know it's rude to reach out for the cakes? Haven't you got a tongue?

GIRL: *Yes, but my arm's longer.*

What's green, weighs a ton and can float in a glass of martini?
An olivephant.

DOCTOR: *I'm afraid you've only got three minutes left to live.*

PATIENT: Is there nothing you can do for me?

DOCTOR: *I could boil you an egg.*

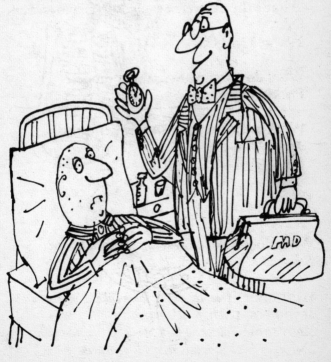

What vegetable should you pick to go with jacket potatoes?
Button mushrooms.

Woman to greengrocer: One pound of mixed nuts, and not too many coconuts please.

How do you make a potato puff?
Chase it round the garden.

What does a skeleton serve his dinner on?
Bone china.

FIRST GIRL: *Here, try one of these cakes I've just made.*
SECOND GIRL: *Urgh, it's horrible!*
FIRST GIRL: *You've no taste. It definitely says in my cookery book that this recipe is delicious.*

What is a breakfast food for orphans?
One with snap crackle but no pop.

What's a good way of putting on weight?
Eat a peach, swallow the centre and you've gained a stone.

What has twenty-two legs and goes crunch crunch crunch?
A football team eating crisps.

What jam can't you eat?
Traffic jam.

What's grey and comes at you from all sides?
Stereophonic porridge.

What's orange and comes out of the ground at 100mph?
A jet-propelled carrot.

Meanwhile, in the cafe,
it's service with a smile...

Waiter, what do you call this?
– It's cottage pie.
Well I've just bitten a piece of the door.

Waiter, have you got any asparagus?
– *We don't serve sparrers, and my name's not Gus.*

Waiter, this meal is terrible. Call the manager.
– *He won't eat it either, sir.*

Waiter, what's wrong with this fish?
– *Long time, no sea.*

Waiter, what's this fly doing in my alphabet soup?
– *I expect he's learning to read.*

Waiter, this tea tastes like dishwater.
— *Drink dishwater often do we sir?*

Waiter, there's a fly in my soup.
— *Don't worry sir, he won't drink much.*

Waiter, you've brought me the wrong order.
— *Well you said you wanted something different.*

Waiter, this bun tastes of soap.
— *That's right sir, it's a bath bun.*

Waiter, do I have to sit here until I die of starvation?
— *No sir, we close at seven.*

Waiter, these eggs are bad.
— *Don't blame me, I only laid the table.*

Waiter, I'd like a little game?
— *Tiddlywinks?*

Waiter, this soup tastes funny.
— *So, why aren't you laughing?*

Waiter, there's a dead fly in my soup.
— *What do you expect for 15p, a live one?*

Waiter, you're not fit to serve a pig!
— *I'm doing my best sir.*

Waiter, what's this in my soup?
— *I don't know sir, all these insects look the same to me.*

Waiter, can I have some undercooked chips, cold beans,
and a fried egg coated in grease?
– I'm sorry sir, we couldn't possibly give you
anything like that.
Why not? You did yesterday.

Waiter, your tie is in my soup.
– *That's all right sir, it's unshrinkable.*

Waiter, there's a flea in my soup.
– *I'll tell him to hop it.*

Waiter, why has this lobster only got one claw?
– It was in a fight.
Well, take it away and bring me the winner.

Waiter, what's this fly doing in my soup?
– *It looks like the backstroke.*

Waiter, there's a twig in my soup.
– *Hold on sir, I'll call the branch manager.*

Waiter, there's a fly in my soup.
– *Don't worry, I've sent for the RSPCA.*

Waiter, there's a dead fly in my soup.
– *Yes sir, it's the hot water that kills them.*

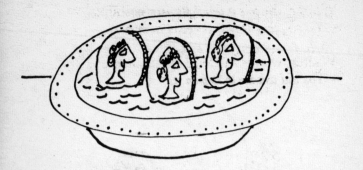

Waiter, there are some coins in my soup.
— *Well you said you wanted some change in our meals.*

Waiter, bring me a glass of milk and a Dover sole.
— Fillet?
Yes, to the brim.

Waiter, is this all you've got to eat?
—*No sir, I'll be having a nice meat pie when I get home.*

Waiter, if this is cod then I'm an idiot.
— *You're right sir, it is cod.*

Waiter, how long will my sausages be?
— *About four inches.*

Waiter, what's this?
— It's bean soup, sir.
I don't care what it was, I want to know what it is now.

Waiter, how long have you been here?
— Six months, sir.
Then it can't have been you who took my order.

Waiter, there's a dead fly in my soup.
— *Yes sir, they're not very good swimmers.*

Waiter, why is my food all mushed up?
— *You did ask me to step on it.*

Waiter, there's a button in my potato.
— *Well what do you expect, it's been cooked in its jacket.*

Waiter, there's a fly in my soup.
— *Don't worry sir, that spider on your bread will get him.*

Waiter, is there soup on the menu?
— *No sir, I wiped it off.*

Waiter, there's a fly in my soup.
— *Keep quiet about it or everyone will want one.*

Waiter, I've just found a maggot in my salad.
— *Well it's better than finding half a maggot, isn't it?*

Waiter, I'll have an egg. No, make that a steak.
— *I'm a waiter sir, not a magician.*

Waiter, there's a bird in my soup.
— *That's right sir, it's bird's-nest soup.*

Waiter, there's a fly in my soup.
— *You'll have to get it out yourself, I can't swim.*

Waiter, are you in the Union?
— *Yes sir, I'm the chop steward.*

Waiter, this plate is wet.
— *That's your soup, sir.*

Waiter, this coffee tastes like mud.
— *I'm not surprised, it was ground only this morning.*

Waiter, I've only got one piece of meat.
— *Hang on sir, I'll cut it in two for you.*

*Waiter, bring me a crocodile sandwich, and make it
snappy.*

Waiter, I'd like a steak, please.
— Would you like anything with it?
*If it's anything like the last one I had here you'd better
bring me a hammer and chisel.*

Waiter, there's a dead fly in my wine.
— *Well you did ask for something with a little body in it.*

Waiter, bring me an elephant-ear sandwich.
— *I'm sorry sir, we've run out of bread.*

Waiter, your thumb's in my soup.
— *That's all right sir, it's not hot.*

Waiter, this beef casserole is terrible.
— I'll have you know the chef put his heart into
that.
I wish he'd put some beef in it too.

Waiter, have you got frogs' legs?
— *No sir, I always walk like this.*

Waiter, what's the meaning of this fly in my soup?
— *I don't know sir, I don't tell fortunes.*

Waiter, do you serve crabs?
— *Sit down sir, we serve anybody.*

Waiter, I'd like coffee, please.
— *With cream or without, sir.*
Without.
— *Actually sir, we don't have any cream. Will you have it without milk?*

Waiter, have you got a wine list?
— *No sir, it's just that one leg is shorter than the other.*

Waiter, have you got frogs' legs?
– Yes sir.
Good, then hop over the counter and get me a sandwich.

Waiter, this coffee tastes like soap.
– I'm afraid there's been a mistake, that must be tea.
The coffee tastes like burnt paper.

Waiter, there's a fly in my soup.
– Yes sir, the chef used to be a tailor.

Waiter, do you call this a three-course meal?
– Of course sir – two chips and one pea.

Waiter, I'll have the soup and then the fish.
– I'd have the fish first if I were you sir, it's just about to go off.

Waiter, I can't eat this.
– Why not?
You haven't given me a knife and fork.

Waiter, what kind of bird is this?
– It's a wood pigeon.
I thought so – bring me a saw.

Waiter, will the pancakes be long?
– No sir, round.

Waiter, what's this fly doing in my soup?
– It looks like it's trying to get out.

Waiter, there's a fly in my butter.
– No there isn't
Yes there is.
– I tell you there isn't for two reasons: one, it's a moth, and two, it's not butter, it's margarine.

Waiter, I'll pay my bill now.
— This pound note's bad, sir.
So was the meal.

Waiter, why is this chop so tough?
— *It's a karate chop.*

Waiter, there's a spider in my soup.
— *That'll be twenty pence extra.*

Waiter, send the chef here. I want to complain
about this disgusting dinner.
— *I'm sorry sir, he's just popped out for his lunch.*

Waiter, this egg tastes strong.
— *Don't worry sir, the tea's nice and weak.*

Waiter, what do you charge for dinner?
— Five pounds per head.
Then just bring me an ear.

How did you find your roast beef, sir?
— *I looked under a potato and there it was.*

Waiter, how long will my spaghetti be?
— *No idea sir, we never measure it.*

Waiter, there's a button in my soup.
— *I expect it fell off when the salad was dressing.*

Waiter, there's a frog in my soup.
— *Yes sir, the fly's on holiday.*

Waiter, this restaurant must have a very clean kitchen.
— Thank you sir, but how did you know?
Everything tastes of soap.

Waiter, there's a fly playing in my saucer.
— *Yes sir, next week he hopes to be playing in the cup.*

Waiter, why have you given me my dinner in a feedbag?
— *The manager says you eat like a horse, sir.*

Waiter, there's a fly in my soup.
— *Yes sir, they don't care what they eat, do they.*

Waiter, there's a fly in my soup.
— *No sir, that's the last customer. The chef's a witch doctor.*

Waiter, there's a cockroach in my soup.
— *That's odd, it's usually a fly.*

DINER: (to waiter scratching his bottom): I say waiter, have you got an itchy bottom?
WAITER: *No sir, only what's on the menu.*

With special thanks to all those who contributed:

Yasmin Akhtar
Deirdre Anderson
Nicholas Anderson
Lesley Arch
David Ash
Michael Atkinson
Jason Austin

Steven Bailey
Tracey Bailey
Mandy Bayley
John Basquill
David Bellis
Frances Betts
Danny Betts
Julia Bevan
Emma Boag
Tracey Brimmell
John Bristow
Louise Bush
Mark Butler

Melanie Cavanagh
Mandy Chase
Gerald Clarke
Nigel Clarke
Christine Clay
Craig Colbert
Tanya Colbert
Gary Coleman
Neil Cooke
Joseph Cooper
Karen Corrigan
Philip Cox

Mark Dalton
Simon Davies
Alison Davis
Rachel Dee

Wendy Dobing
John Downie

Duncan Eldridge
Sam Ellams
Susan Evans
Walter Evans

Tracey Fidgett
Russell Fidgett
John Ford
Sheila Fullerton

Wayne Gallagher
Deborah Gee
Emma Goodwin
Paulette Goodwin
Richard Gray
Claire Greeley
John Greenfield
Trevor Griffiths

Ian Hall
Peter Hancock
Sophie Harris
Anna Harrison
Tracey Hart
David Higgs
Vanessa Hill
Natasha Hodges
Steven Holder
Tracey Holland
Wendy Holliday
Kirst Hudson
George Hughes
Lisa Hutton
Jamie Hymus

Natalie Jenkins

Eric Jones
Shane Just

Stuart Keates
Deana King
Christopher Knight
Gail Knight

Edwin Law
Jonathan Lawrence
Sarah Lee
Debbie Lloyd
Karen Loasby
Wilhelmina Lyle

Karen McDonald
Sue McMichael
Richard Mayze
Trevor Miles
Terea Moore
Donna Morrice

Neena Nandy
Mark Newton
Andrew Nolan
Samantha North
Patrick Nunn

Nicola Park
Chris Parks
Louise Parsons
Anthony Pearce
Helen Pember
Neil Peterson
Liz Phillips
Joanne Pleat
Dawn Potter
Hazel Price

Jonathon Quinn

Rachel Ramsden
Alison Randall
Emma Randall
Josie Randall
Julia Rattray
Gary Rees
Dawn Reynolds
Paul Riddell
Sally Roberts
Gary Robinson
Derek Ross
Debbie Ross

Anjli Sachdev

Syreeta Saur
Teresa Scully
Helen Searing
Caroline Sessions
Sara Shorthouse
Jason Sidebotham
Andrew Smith
Martin Smith
Kristian Stephenson

Peter Tate
John Taylor
Philip Tew
Stephen Thackray
Mark Thompson
Scott Thompson

Linda Tracey
Ngoi Phuong Tran

David Vigrass

Julia Walker
David Walsh
Kevin Waters
Laura Watts
Kerry Webb
Mark Williams
Alyson Wills
Claire Wilson
Stuart Wilson
David Winterflood